Disney

Young Readers
COLLECTION

Bendon Publishing, International
Ashland, Ohio

Disney

Young Readers
COLLECTION

Table of Contents

FLASH CARD INSTRUCTIONS

The flash cards at the end of each story will help your child learn to recognize and practice frequently used words. First, carefully cut out the flash cards. Then, choose three to five cards at a time. Say the word on each card. Then, ask your child to repeat each word. Once your child masters these words, move through the pile in the same manner, continuing to review the words learned earlier.

There are a few other ways for you and your child to use these flash cards for extra practice. Here are a few suggestions:

- Pick the Word—Lay out 5-10 flash cards on a table. Then, say one of the words on the cards. Ask your child to point to the word you've said.
- Make a Sentence—Invite your child to make a sentence from the sight word cards. Have your child look at the illustrations in the story for ideas. Then, have your child choose another card and substitute it for one of the cards in the sentence. Ask your child how the new word changes the meaning of the sentence.
- My Own Sight Words—Have your child make his or her own sight word cards using the writing lines on the back of the cards. Help your child write words that he or she might use regularly, such as family names, your street, your town, or your state. Once your child is able to identify and recognize these words, add them to the "Make a Sentence" game above.

The flash cards in this collection can also be a useful tool as your child completes the activities at the end of each story. If a particular activity seems difficult for your child, use the flash cards to practice the activity first before your child writes.

Winnie the Pooh

The Big
Honeypot Rescue

Adapted by Linda Armstrong

The Big
Honeypot Rescue

Table of Contents

Pooh wanted **to** go to sleep. But the wind was blowing too hard outside. There was a very strange noise. It was very close.

"Grrrr!" **went** the noise.

Pooh was afraid to go to the door and **see** what was out there.

"Piglet," **he** said. "Is that you?"

"Grrrr!" went the noise. Pooh had to find out what it was.

He went to see.

A big orange thing was **not** far from Pooh's door. The thing had black stripes. It bounced right on top of **Pooh**.

"Hoo-hoo-hoo! I am **Tigger**," said the thing.

"You scared me!" Pooh said.

"I **know** I **did**," Tigger said.

Pooh did not know Tigger.

"Tiggers do **not** hurt bears. Tiggers just bounce!" Tigger said.

"**I** am glad," **Pooh** said.

Tigger went to the door. "Watch out tonight," he said. "There are strange things in the woods."

"What strange things?" Pooh asked.

"Why, heffalumps and woozles, of course!" Tigger **said**. "They **will** eat honey if you **let them**."

"I will not let them," said Pooh.

Pooh wanted to watch for heffalumps and woozles. But **it** was too hard for him to stay awake.

After the noisy wind stopped, rain started to fall outside.

Pooh went to sleep. **He** dreamed a heffalump **ran** away with his honey. Pooh thought the monster was real.

He ran after it.

When Pooh woke up the heffalump was gone. But the little bear had a different problem. His house was full of water. "Oh, no!" Pooh said. "My honey!"

He opened the door, but the water did not run **out**. It **got** closer and closer to Pooh's honeypots. He picked **them** up.

He got them out.

Pooh put his honeypots in a safe place outside. He did **not** want to get water in his honey.

Just then, **Piglet** floated by. Piglet **was** sitting in a chair. "Are you **all right**, Piglet?" asked Pooh.

Piglet was not all right.

Poor Piglet floated right out of his house, but he was smart.
He put a note in a bottle. His friends found the note.
They all looked for **him**. Owl **saw** Piglet right away.
"Do not worry, Piglet," **Owl** said. "We will help you."
Pooh had fallen into the water, too. He was harder to
find because his head was stuck in a honeypot.

Owl saw him.

Owl flew above the two friends for a better **look**. "Somebody has to help," he **said**. "Who, who, who can help?"

Pooh and Piglet were headed for a big waterfall. They went right over. At the bottom, Pooh was in Piglet's chair, and Piglet was in Pooh's honeypot.

Christopher Robin saw that Piglet was safe.

"Look!" said Christopher Robin.

"Pooh **found** Piglet!" Christopher Robin said. "We should have a hero party for **him**!"

Then the friends all cheered. "Yes! Oh, yes!" they said.

"I will get a cake," Christopher Robin said. "What kind of cake do you want, Pooh?"

Then Pooh said, "If it is all right with you, I would like **some** –"

Pooh always wanted the same thing. His friends knew what it was.

"Honey!" they said. **They** all laughed.

Then they found him some.

Say the word at the top of each box. Then fill in the missing letters.

see	went
__ __	__ __
__ ee	we __ __
__ __	__ __
s __ __ __	__ __ nt

Read the words in the box. Then read the sentences. Find the word in the box that correctly completes each sentence. Write the word on the line.

_____

I want _____ go.

_____

I want to _____ it!

_____

_____ went to see it.

_____

Pooh _____ to see what was there.

see
to
went
He

Trace the names with your pencil. Then write the names on your own.

Pooh

Tigger

Read the words in the box. Then read the sentences. Find the word in the box that correctly completes each sentence. Write the word on the line.

_____ did not know Tigger.

_____ did not hurt Pooh.

I _____ him.

I _____ not do it!

| know |
| Pooh |
| Tigger |
| did |

27

Read the words in the box. Then read the sentences. Find the word in the box that correctly completes each sentence. Write the word on the line.

_____

_____ am not Pooh.

You are _____ Pooh.

not
let
will
I
said

He _____ not let them do that.

Pooh will not _____ them do it.

"I will let them do it," Pooh _____.

28

Say the word at the top of each box. Then fill in the missing letters.

after	ran
a___er	r__n
af_____	__an

Read the words in the box. Then read the sentences. Find the word in the box that correctly completes each sentence. Write the word on the line.

_____

He ran _____ it.

_____

He _____ away.

_____

_____ ran after him.

ran
after
He

Say the word at the top of each box. Then fill in the missing letters.

out	got
ou __	**go** __
__ __ **t**	__ __ **t**

Read the words in the box. Then read the sentences. Find the word in the box that correctly completes each sentence. Write the word on the line.

He _____ them.

_____ did not run.

He did not want _____ .

They ran _____ of the house.

He
out
got
them

30

Say the word at the top of each box. Then fill in the missing letters.

right	all
r _ _ _ _ _ _ _ ight	a _ _ _ _ _ _ a _ _
was	not
w _ _ _ _ a _	n _ _ _ _ _ t

Say the name or word at the top of each box. Then fill in the missing letters.

Owl	saw
O _ l	sa _
O _ _	s _ _

Read the words in the box. Then read the sentences. Find the word in the box that correctly completes each sentence. Write the word on the line.

_____

_____ saw him.

_____

Owl _____ Pooh.

_____

Pooh saw _____ .

saw
him
Owl

Trace the name with your pencil. Then write the name on your own.

Christopher Robin

Christopher Robin

Christopher _____

Read the words in the box. Then read the sentences. Find the word in the box that correctly completes each sentence. Write the word on the line.

Robin
said
Look

"_____

_____

_____ at me," Tigger said.

_____

"I do not know you," Owl _____.

_____

Christopher _____ went to see Owl.

Say the word at the top of each box. Then fill in the missing letters.

found

f _ _ _ nd

_ _ _ _ _
_ ou _ _ _

some

_ _ _ _
s _ _ _ e

_ _ _ _
_ _ _ me

him

_ _ _
h _ _ m

_ _ _
_ im

then

_ _ _ _
_ _ _ en

_ _ _ _
t _ _ n

they

_ _ _ _
_ _ _ ey

_ _ _ _
t _ _ y

Christopher Robin

Piglet

I

Tigger

found

him

all

after

Pooh

Owl

they

he

it

saw

then

some

see

let

got

was

said

right

to

went

did

look

will

ran

them

know

not

out

Winnie the Pooh

The
Blustery Day

Written by Teddy Slater
Adapted by Linda Armstrong

The Blustery Day

Table of Contents

One blustery **fall** day, Piglet was sweeping up **a big** pile of leaves in front of his door.

No matter how many leaves Piglet swept away, the blustery fall **wind** blew more back. Piglet was busy, but the wind was busier. **What** a busy, blustery wind!

What a big fall wind!

"Oh, dear," **Piglet said**. "What shall **I** d-d-do? I asked my friend **Pooh** to **come here** for tea. He is on his way. Just look at all of these leaves! I will never finish sweeping in time."

"Here I come, Piglet," said Pooh.

Suddenly, the big wind got even bigger. It lifted Piglet right up off the ground. Pooh saw his friend just in time.

"Don't worry. I **will** save you," **Pooh** said.

Pooh grabbed Piglet's scarf.

"**I** h-hope you can **hold on**," Piglet **said**.

The wind pulled Pooh along. The scarf started to unravel.

"I will hold on," Pooh said.

"Mama!" Roo **said**. "Come and look at the funny kite!"
"Oh, dear!" Kanga said. "That is not a kite. That is Piglet!"
"I hope Pooh can **hold on**!" Roo said.
The big wind pulled Piglet and Pooh along. That blustery wind just kept getting bigger and bigger. Kanga and Roo wanted to help. But **they** could not.

"Hold on! Hold on!" they said.

That big wind lifted Pooh right off the ground. Pooh was afraid. But he did **not** let go of the string. He did not **want** the wind to carry **Piglet** away.

There was a big tree right in front of them. And there was a house in the tree.

"Pooh, where does the wind t-t-take things?" Piglet asked.

"**I do** not know," Pooh **said**. "But I think we are going **to** find out."

"I do not want to," Piglet said.

Owl saw two faces pressed against his window. He was very surprised.

"Who-who-who is there?" **Owl** asked.

"It's m-m-me," Piglet **said**.

"And me, too," Pooh said. "We were passing by, and we just dropped **in**."

"Why did you **come** on such a bad day?" Owl asked. "It is windy out there. You could get hurt." Between gusts, Owl opened his door wide.

"Come in," Owl said. "Come in."

"Please, make yourselves at home," Owl **said**. "I do not get much company here, but I do enjoy visitors."

Pooh and Piglet sat down.

Owl pulled out a teapot and some cups. "**Would** you **like some** tea? **I** have some honey, **too**."

Piglet nodded yes.

"I would like some, too," Pooh said.

"Your visit," Owl said, "reminds me of something. **It** was during the Great Wind of '67. My great-aunt Clara went **with** her sister to–"

They did not hear the end of Owl's story. The big wind blew up a bigger gust. Owl's tree house shook. Pooh and Piglet were afraid. The whole house tipped to one side. It tipped so far it **came down**. Piglet, Pooh, and Owl were still inside.

They came down with it.

"**Did** you hear that crash?" Christopher Robin asked.
Rabbit and Eeyore nodded.

"I think it came from Owl's tree," Rabbit said.

They hurried over to help, but Pooh **and** the others had already climbed out.

"Don't worry, Owl," Christopher Robin said. "We will find a new house for you."

"We sure will," all the friends said.

And they did.

Trace the words with a pencil.
Then write the words on your own.

Fall

fall

Wind

wind

Trace the names with your pencil. Then write the names on your own.

Pooh

Piglet

Read the words in the box. Then read the sentences. Find the word in the box that correctly completes each sentence. Write the word on the line.

_____ is here.

Here is _____ .

_____ here," I said.

_____ will come.

| Come |
| Piglet |
| Pooh |
| I |

Say the word at the top of each box. Then fill in the missing letters.

will

w _ _ l
_ _ ll

on

o _ _
_ _ _

hold

ho _ _
_ o _ d

said

s _ _ d
_ _ id

Pooh

P _ _ h
_ _ oh

Trace the words with your pencil. Then write the words on your own.

Hold

hold

Read the words in the box. Then read the sentences. Find the word in the box that correctly completes each sentence. Write the word on the line.

"Hold on," they _____.

_____ did hold on.

They will _____ on.

They did hold _____.

hold
They
said
on

Say the word at the top of each box. Then fill in the missing letters.

not

n _ _ t

_ _ _ t

_ _ t

do

d _ _ _

_ _ _ _

to

t _ _ _

_ _ _ _

_ _ _ _

want

w _ _ _ t

_ _ _ t

_ _ nt

said

s _ _ d

_ _ id

Trace the name.

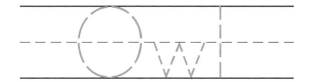

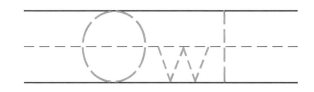

Fill in the missing letters.

Write the name.

Read the words in the box. Then read the sentences. Find the word in the box that correctly completes each sentence. Write the word on the line.

said
too
Pooh
would
like

_____

I like _____ .

_____

Pooh would _____ some.

_____

I _____ like some, too.

_____

"I want some _____," Pooh said.

_____

"I like Piglet," Pooh _____ .

Say the word at the top of each box. Then fill in the missing letters.

they

t _ _ y

_ _ _

_ ey

came

c _ _ e

_ _ me

down

do _ _ _

_ o _ n

with

wi _ _ _

_ i _ h

it

i _

_ _ _

71

Say the word at the top of each box. Then fill in the missing letters.

not

n __ t

__ __ t

do

d __ __

__ __ __

to

t __ __

__ __ __

they

t __ __ y

th __ __ __

did

__ __ d

__ __ id

72

came

wind

I

Owl

Pooh

in

what

big

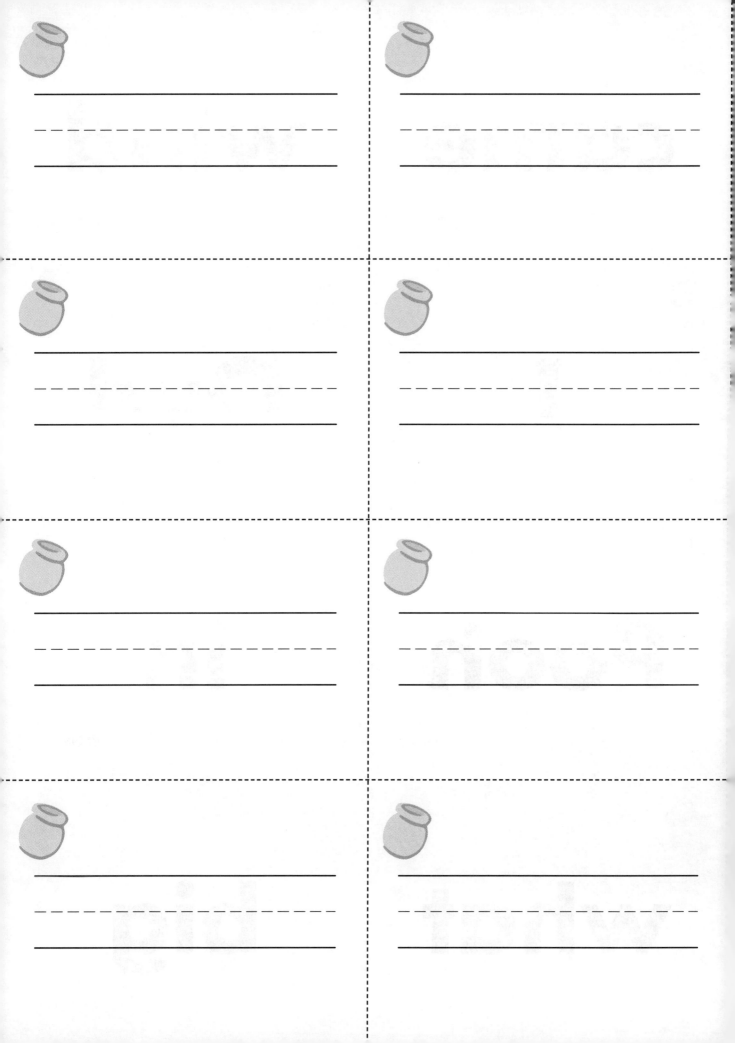

it

said

Piglet

they

on

he

down

with

a

not

fall

here

come

want

hold

like

too

and

some

to

will

do

did

would

Winnie the Pooh

Pooh Helps Out

Written by Kathleen W. Zoehfeld
Adapted by Linda Armstrong

Winnie the Pooh

Pooh Helps Out

Table of Contents

Winnie the **Pooh** sat on the bed in his cozy little house and looked around.

"What shall I do? **Let me** see. I **think** I will do nothing at all," he **said**.

He hummed a little nothing hum. "Hum de dum."

But after a while nothing to do began to feel quite bothersome

"Let me think," Pooh said.

I **will** go over to Piglet's house, Pooh thought.

"I need your **help**, Piglet," **Pooh said**. "I have been doing nothing by myself, but I do not like it. It would be fun to do nothing with a friend. Will **you** please do nothing with me?"

Piglet wanted to do nothing with Pooh, but first he had to **wash** his dishes.

"I will help you wash," Pooh said.

Soon Piglet and Pooh **were done**. They sat down to do nothing. Piglet yawned.

Doing nothing was still not a lot of fun, so Pooh and Piglet went to see Owl.

"Owl!" Pooh called. "Would you like us to help you with anything?"

"Who-who-who said that?" Owl asked.

"I did! I want to help you," said Pooh. "Piglet wants to help, too."

"What a wonderful idea. I know my dusting would be easy with two friends to help."

They cleaned and dusted and dusted and cleaned.

Soon they were done.

So they all went to Tigger's house.

"This is great! Just the guys I wanted to see!" Tigger said. "I hope you like to **clean**. I do not like to pick up my toys. But **it** will be fun with three good friends who want to help."

Soon they finished. Pooh looked around. Tigger's room **was** not the same.

It was clean.

Next, they headed over to Eeyore's house.

"Oh, look!" Everyone gasped.

Eeyore's house had fallen down.

"**You** just need help," Pooh **said**. "You **are** lucky. We are **very good** at helping."

Pooh, Piglet, Owl, and Tigger helped **Eeyore** fix his house.

"You are very good," Eeyore said.

Pooh patted his tummy. "Time **for** something to eat," he **said**.

Tigger laughed. "**We** all want to eat. We **will** go over to Rabbit's house. He will be cooking supper."

"I would like to help **you**," Rabbit said when they got there. "I have a garden full of vegetables. But I'm too tired to **pick them**."

"We will pick them for you," Pooh said.

Soon big juicy tomatoes, crunchy carrots, and snappy beans filled Rabbit's kitchen counter. Potatoes **were** already cooking in a big, steaming pot. **They** smelled very good.

"Are you **ready**?" Rabbit asked. "We will eat supper soon."

They were ready.

While Rabbit finished cooking, **Pooh**, Piglet, Owl, Tigger, and Eeyore set the table.

When everyone was sitting down, Rabbit brought in a big bowl of stew.

"**This** supper **is** for my five **good** friends," Rabbit **said**. "I could never have made it without you."

"This is good!" Pooh said.

After **that** wonderful supper, Pooh **and** Piglet sat in their thoughtful spot. **They** were warm and tired and happy.

"We **did** so much today," Pooh said. "**What** shall we do now?"

"How about just doing nothing," Piglet suggested.

"Yes, that **is** a good idea," Pooh said. "We will do nothing."

And that is what they did.

Say the word at the top of each box. Then fill in the missing letters.

me

m _ _

_ _ _

_ _ _

Pooh

P _ _ _ h

_ _ _ _ _

_ _ oh

let

l _ t

_ _ _

_ e _

said

_ _ _

sa _ _ _

_ _ _ a _ d

think

th _ _ k

_ _ _

_ _ in _

102

Read the words in the box. Then read the sentences. Find the word in the box that correctly completes each sentence. Write the word on the line.

| **will** |
| **Pooh** |
| **said** |
| **help** |
| **I** |

_____

Piglet will _____ .

" _____

_____ will help Piglet," Pooh said.

_____

"I need help," _____ said.

_____

Piglet _____ help Pooh.

_____

"I like Piglet," Pooh _____ .

Trace the words with your pencil. Then write the words on your own.

_____   _____

was   _____

will   _____

_____   _____

Read the words in the box. Then read the sentences. Find the word in the box that correctly completes each sentence. Write the word on the line.

Pooh was _____.

Soon they _____ done.

They will come _____.

_____ wanted to help.

They
done
were
soon

Trace the words with your pencil.
Then write the words on your own.

it

was

clean

Read the words in the box. Then read the sentences. Find
the word in the box that correctly completes each sentence.
Write the word on the line.

Will he help _____ it up?

Pooh _____ there.

_____ was clean.

| It |
| clean |
| was |

Say the word at the top of each box. Then fill in the missing letters.

you

o

y _ u

good

g _ _ _ d

_ _ _ od

are

a _ _ e

_ r _

said

sa _ _ _

_ a _ d

Eeyore

Ee _ _ re

_ _ yo _ e

ACTIVITY 6

Trace the words with your pencil. Then write the words on your own.

them

pick

Read the words in the box. Then read the sentences. Find the word in the box that correctly completes each sentence. Write the word on the line.

_____ want that, too.

Pooh will _____ them.

_____ can do it.

"I like you," Pooh _____ .

You will pick _____ for Pooh.

pick
We
said
them
Pooh

107

Trace the words with your pencil.
Then write the words on your own.

they

were

ready

Read the words in the box. Then read the sentences. Find
the word in the box that correctly completes each sentence.
Write the word on the line.

He was _____ .

| ready |
| were |
| They |

_____ were ready to go.

Piglet and Pooh _____ ready.

Say the word at the top of each box.
Then fill in the missing letters.

Pooh

P___h
_____
___oh

this

th___
_____
___is

said

sa___
_____
__a_d

good

g___d
_____
___oo

is

i___
_____
_____

Trace the words with your pencil. Then write the words on your own.

and

what

Read the words in the box. Then read the sentences. Find the word in the box that correctly completes each sentence. Write the word on the line.

_____ that Pooh?

They _____ it.

What is _____?

_____ did they do?

Pooh _____ Piglet did that.

| did |
| **What** |
| **and** |
| **Is** |
| **that** |

good

it

are

Eeyore

clean

help

this

will

what

ready

Pooh

were

think

done

did

that

for

me

I

pick

is

and

they

soon

them

let

wash

you

said

was

very

we

Winnie the Pooh

Pooh's Honey Tree

Adapted by Linda Armstrong

Pooh's Honey Tree

Table of Contents

All of Pooh's honey pots were empty. Poor Pooh! **He** did not **know** where to find more honey.

He sat down. "**Now I** have to think, think, think," he **said**.

Just then a bee came by. Buzz!

Pooh smiled.

"Now I know!" he said.

"Bees have honey," **Pooh** said.

The bee flew into the woods, **and** Pooh ran after him. The bee **went** into a hole high **up** in one of the trees. Pooh could not fly, but he could climb.

Pooh went up and up and up.

Pooh sat on a branch just
under the hole. The branch was
very small. **It** was **much** too high up
for a bear.

"Are you home, bees? Please come out. I need
your **help**," said Pooh.

"Buzz!" the bees said. They **did not** come out.

The branch began to shake. Pooh held on.

It did not help very much.

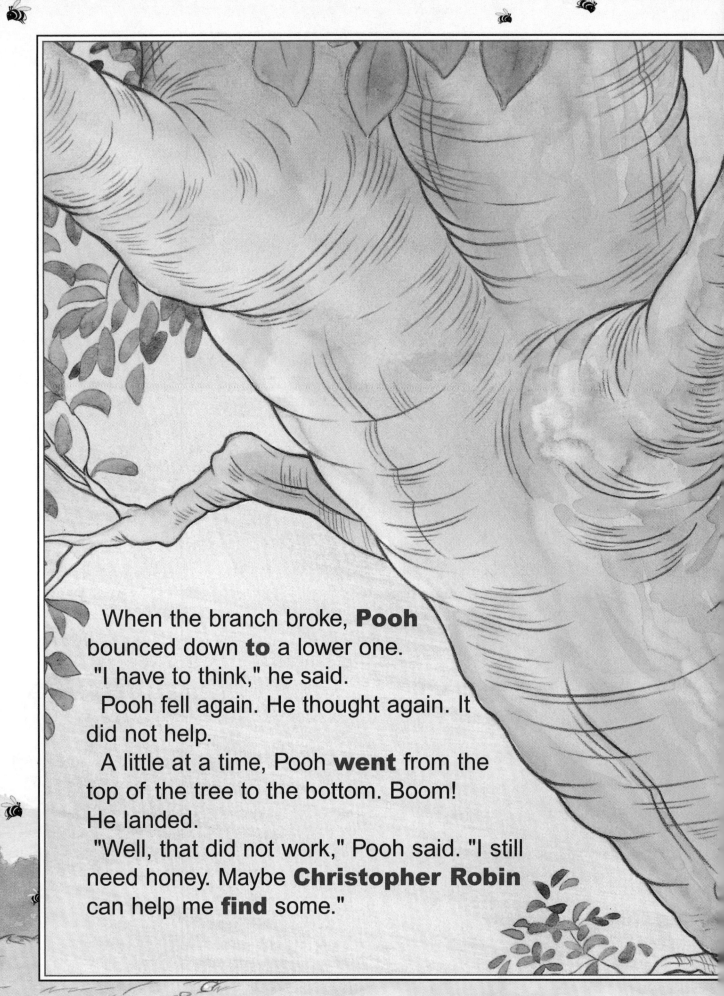

When the branch broke, **Pooh** bounced down **to** a lower one. "I have to think," he said.

Pooh fell again. He thought again. It did not help.

A little at a time, Pooh **went** from the top of the tree to the bottom. Boom! He landed.

"Well, that did not work," Pooh said. "I still need honey. Maybe **Christopher Robin** can help me **find** some."

Pooh went to find Christopher Robin.

When Pooh found him, he was in the woods with Kanga, Roo, Owl and Eeyore.

"**I** was wondering," **said** Pooh. "Do you have a balloon?"

"Yes, I **do**," Christopher Robin said. "But why do you need a balloon?"

"**Well**, I would like to get some honey," **Pooh** said. His voice was very soft. He did not want the bees to hear.

"You do not get honey with a balloon," Christopher Robin said.

"Well, I do," said Pooh.

"**I** have a plan," Pooh **said**. "I will roll in the mud. Then I will hang onto the balloon and float past the honey tree. I will look like a little, dark cloud. Then **you** can **help**. You can open your umbrella and talk about rain. We **will** fool the bees."

Christopher Robin listened.

"I will help you," said Christopher Robin.

Pooh rolled around in the mud. He held onto the balloon and pointed to a tree.

"Push me up!" he said. "The bees are up there. I will get close to **them**."

The balloon floated high up in the tree. Pooh **came** close to the hole. He took **out** some honey.

All of the bees were quiet. Then, suddenly, buzz, buzz, buzz!

All of them came out.

Bees were everywhere. Buzz, buzz, buzz! They flew **down fast**. They flew all around **Pooh**.

"I think they know something is wrong," said Pooh.

The string on the balloon **came** loose. The balloon ran out of air.

Pooh came down fast.

"Quick! Jump in the mud with me!" said Christopher Robin.
He opened his **old** umbrella. Pooh crawled under it. They
felt **silly** sitting in the mud. But it was a safe place to wait
for the bees to go away. They waited a long time.
 "I think the bees knew you were really a **bear**,"
Christopher Robin said when the last one was gone.
 "It was a good plan," Pooh **said**. "But those were the
wrong bees."

"Silly old bear," said Christopher Robin.

Say the word at the top of each box. Then fill in the missing letters.

now

n___

___ow

I

know

k___w

kn___

he

___e

h___

said

___ai___

___d

Trace the word with your pencil. Then write the word on your own.

Pooh

Read the words in the box. Then read the sentences. Find the word in the box that correctly completes each sentence. Write the word on the line.

_____ ran after him.

He _____ to the woods.

He ran _____ ran.

Pooh went _____ there.

and
Pooh
up
went

141

Say the word at the top of each box. Then fill in the missing letters.

did

___
___ i ___
___

d ___ d

help

___
___ elp
___

h ___ p

Read the words in the box. Then read the sentences. Find the word in the box that correctly completes each sentence. Write the word on the line.

He _____ not help.

It did _____ help.

He did _____ .

He did _____ .

| not |
| it |
| help |
| did |

Say the word at the top of each box. Then fill in the missing letters.

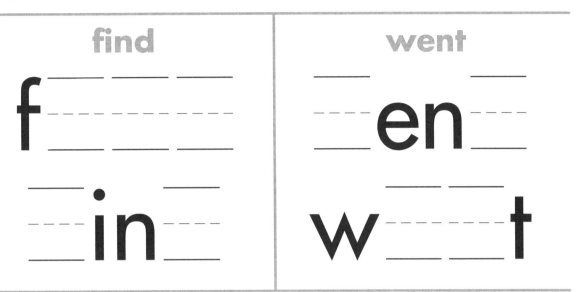

find

f _ _ _
_ in _

went

_ _ en _
w _ _ _ t

Read the words in the box. Then read the sentences. Find the word in the box that correctly completes each sentence. Write the word on the line.

_____

Pooh went to _____ him.

| find |
| to |
| went |

_____

Christopher Robin_____ to find him.

_____

Pooh went _____ find Christopher Robin.

ACTIVITY 5

Read the words in the box. Then read the sentences. Find the word in the box that correctly completes each sentence. Write the word on the line.

"_____
_____
_____, I will do it," said Pooh.

_____
_____
_____ you want to do it?

Yes, _____ do.

_____
_____
_____ will do it.

_____
_____
"I will," _____ Pooh.

I

said

Well

Do

Pooh

144

Say the word at the top of each box. Then fill in the missing letters.

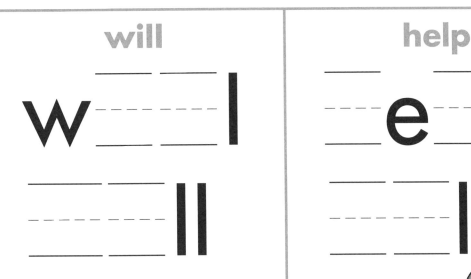

will	help
w ___ l	___ e ___ p
___ ll	___ l

Read the words in the box. Then read the sentences. Find the word in the box that correctly completes each sentence. Write the word on the line.

_____ want to help.

I _____ help, too.

will
help
I

Christopher Robin will _____ .

Say the word at the top of each box. Then fill in the missing letters.

all

l ___ ___

___ ___ ___

___ ___ ___

of

o ___ ___

___ ___ ___

them

___ ___ em

___ ___ ___

___ ___ ___

came

c ___ ___ ___

___ ___ ___

out

___ ___ t

___ ___ t

___ ___ ___

o ___ ___

Say the word at the top of each box. Then fill in the missing letters.

came	down
___ ___ ___me	d___ ___n
c___m___	___o___

Read the words in the box. Then read the sentences. Find the word in the box that correctly completes each sentence. Write the word on the line.

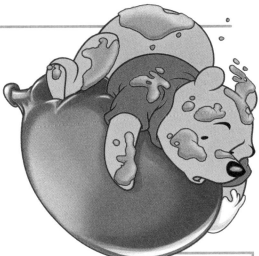

_____

_____ went up and up.

came
Pooh
down

Then Pooh _____ down.

All of them came _____.

ACTIVITY 9

Say the word at the top of each box. Then fill in the missing letters.

bear	**old**
__ __ __ __	__ l __
__ ea __	__ l __
__ __ r	o __ __

Read the words in the box. Then read the sentences. Find the word in the box that correctly completes each sentence. Write the word on the line.

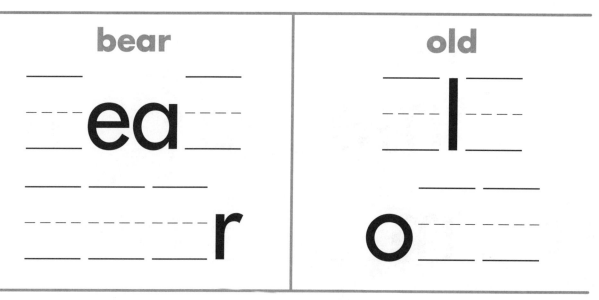

Pooh is a _____ .

" _____

_____ old bear,"

said Christopher Robin.

"I want to help," _____

Christopher Robin.

Silly
said
bear

Christopher Robin

© Disney

Pooh

© Disney

all

© Disney

I

© Disney

up

© Disney

you

© Disney

came

© Disney

and

© Disney

he

bear

it

much

them

down

to

did

help

said

well

of

went

very

not

old

find

do

out

silly

now

will

fast

know

Adapted by Linda Armstrong

Table of Contents

Pongo lived in London. His pet, Roger, wrote songs. The two of them had a good life, but sometimes Pongo was lonely. He **could not let** himself **go** on forever without a family. He wanted to find the right dog and settle down.

One day Pongo was looking out the window. The right dog walked by with her pet. Both of **them** looked perfect.

Pongo could not let them go.

Pongo **went right** over to get his leash. Roger took him for a walk. They went to the park. **Pongo** saw the perfect dog and her pet. The two of **them** were sitting right **by** the pond. Pongo pulled Roger along with him.

Pongo went right by them.

Pongo was right. Perdy **was** perfect, and so was Anita, her pet. When Roger and Anita were married, Pongo and **Perdy** were married, **too**. They were all very happy. It wasn't long before Pongo became a father. He was very proud.

Perdy was, too.

The night the puppies were born, Cruella De Vil knocked on the door. Cruella was an old friend of Anita's. **Roger** did not like her. He did not want **to** let her in.

"**We** have to be polite," Anita **said**.

"This place is too small for so many puppies. You cannot **keep** them," Cruella said. "I will buy **them**. How much do you **want**?" She took out a pen to write a check. She splattered ink all over Roger.

"We want to keep them," said Roger.

One night when Roger and Anita were gone, two men came to the door. "We have to work on the wiring. **It** will only take a few minutes," they said. Nanny **was not** able to stop them. They tied her up.

The two bad men took the puppies far away from Pongo and Perdy. They took them **right** to an old house in the country.

It was not right.

Perdy and Pongo had many friends. They all wanted to **help**. They sent out a message about the puppies. Sergeant Tibs, a country cat, heard puppies barking at the old house. He **came** just in time. He found the puppies. He told them **to** hide under the stairs. He helped them climb out through a hole in the wall. The bad men almost found them.

Perdy and Pongo came to help.

They all got out of the house. Roger was right about Cruella. She had a **cold** heart. She planned to make the puppies into fur coats. The bad men and Cruella did not give up. They drove up and down the road looking for the puppies. Pongo, Perdy, and the puppies had to hide under a bridge until they left. They **were all** tired and hungry.

They were all cold.

They made it to a nearby town. A friend found a truck for Pongo, Perdy, and the puppies to ride home in. They just had to get across the street. **It** was not easy because Cruella and the bad men were watching the street. Pongo thought of a way to get the puppies **across**. They **made** themselves black by rolling in soot.

They made it across.

When **they** came home, Pongo, Perdy, and the puppies were still black. Roger and Anita **did** not know **that** the black dogs were theirs. They did not know **what** to do. Nanny did. She cleaned them off.

"This **is** wonderful! Just look at all of these puppies! Let's buy a Dalmatian plantation," said Roger.

That is what they did.

Say the word at the top of each box. Then fill in the missing letters.

could

c ___ ___ ld

___ ou ___

not

n ___ t

___ o ___

let

___ ___ t

l ___ ___

them

th ___ ___

t ___ ___ m

go

g ___

___ o

Trace the name with your pencil. Then write the name on your own.

Pongo

Read the words in the box. Then read the sentences. Find the word in the box that correctly completes each sentence. Write the word on the line.

Pongo went _____ them.

Pongo was _____.

Pongo _____ too.

Pongo let _____ go.

| went |
| by |
| right |
| them |

Trace the name with your pencil. Then write the name on your own.

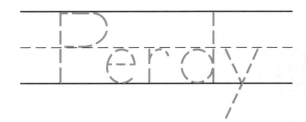

Say the word at the top of each box. Then fill in the missing letters.

was	**too**
__ a __	__ t __ __
w __ __	__ o __

let	
__ et	
__ e	

Read the words in the box. Then read the sentences. Find the word in the box that correctly completes each sentence. Write the word on the line.

_____

We _____ them.

We want to _____ them.

We want _____ go.

"Let them go!" Roger _____.

want
keep
to
said

Say the word at the top of each box. Then fill in the missing letters.

it	right
_ t	_ _ _ _ _
i _	r _ _ _ _ _
	_ i _ _ t

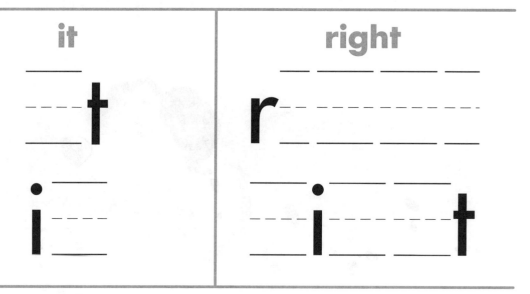

Read the words in the box. Then read the sentences. Find the word in the box that correctly completes each sentence. Write the word on the line.

_____

It was _____.

Pongo _____ right.

It was _____ Pongo.

____ was Roger.

right
was
it
not

Say the word at the top of each box. Then fill in the missing letters.

and

__nd

a__d

came

c__m__

____e

help

he____

__e__p

Say the word at the top of each box. Then fill in the missing letters.

they

___ ___ ___
___ ___ ey
th___ ___

all

___ l
___
a___ ___

Read the words in the box. Then read the sentences. Find the word in the box that correctly completes each sentence. Write the word on the line.

_____

They _____ came.

_____

They were _____.

_____

_____ came to help.

_____

They _____ right.

cold
all
were
They

184

Read the words in the box. Then read the sentences. Find the word in the box that correctly completes each sentence. Write the word on the line.

_____

They _____ it!

_____

They went _____ .

Pongo made ____ too.

_____

_____ could not go.

_____

_____ all came.

_____

Perdy _____ it across.

across

it

made

They

Say the word at the top of each box. Then fill in the missing letters.

that

a

th

is

s

i

what

wh

t

did

d

i

Pongo

said

Perdy

across

they

is

them

could

want

we

by

Roger

was

it

went

were

to

© Disney

not

© Disney

keep

© Disney

go

© Disney

made

© Disney

let

© Disney

that

© Disney

right

© Disney

all

too

and

help

came

did

cold

what

Puppy Parade

Written by Cecilia Venn
Adapted by Linda Armstrong

Puppy Parade

Table of Contents

"**W**ake up, **Perdy**," **said** Pongo. "**We** have to **find** the puppies. We are late for the Puppy Parade."

Perdy yawned. "All right, dear. We **will** look for **them**."

"But where are they?" Pongo asked.

"We will find them," Perdy said.

First Patch stumbled in. He **could not see** where **he** was going. He bumped into Pepper. They fell on top of five sleeping puppies and woke them up. They all romped together in the living room. The lamp almost tipped over. The chair shook. A pillow landed in front of the television set. Lucky started barking.

He could not see.

Perdy wagged her tail and tipped over a bucket. **Five** more puppies spilled out. One **of them** jumped into the laundry basket. Penny was asleep **in there**. Out she hopped. Two puppies **were** playing with the blanket, and they bumped into the clock. The clock door flew open.

Five of them were in there.

The puppies did **not stop**. They romped down the hall and out the door. Five chased after them. Five more ran as fast as **they could**. They slid into the kitchen. They knocked over the mop, the broom, and even the basket.

They could not stop.

The noise woke up some pups taking a nap on the sunny windowsill. **They** jumped down as fast as they **could**. They were **always** ready to have fun. The last one knocked over a plate filled with good things to **eat**. Rolly and his friends came running.

They could always eat.

Perdy sniffed. She heard something scratching and wondered **what it was**. She went over and lifted the rug. Five pups popped out and kissed her on the nose. The other puppies rushed in. They skidded into the rug. The rug hit **a** piano bench. Five more pups were curled up underneath. They jumped up on the piano. They ran back and forth on the keys. They wanted to **show** everyone how to make fine puppy music. Five more puppies sang along.

What a show it was!

There were puppies in the living room, puppies in the kitchen, puppies in the hall. There were puppies everywhere! Pongo counted every one he **could find**.

"5, 10, 15, 20, 25, 30, 35, 40—I **wish** they would stay still," **Pongo** said.

"45, 50, 55, 60, 65, 70, 75, 80, 85, 90—I only see 95 of **them**," he **said**. "Where are the other four?"

"I wish I could find them," Pongo said.

Perdy thought about it.

"I want to **help**, but **I** do not know where they are. **You** cannot find them. Maybe we **will** just have to miss the Puppy Parade," **she said**.

Just then four more puppies fell out of a high shelf. They landed right on top of Pongo. Perdy laughed.

"I will help you," she said.

Pongo counted the puppies again. All 99 were there. They were ready for the Puppy Parade. Then Perdy looked at the calendar.

"**Oh**, **Pongo**!" she **said**. "There is **no** parade today. It is next week!"

"Oh no!" Pongo said.

Trace the name with your pencil. Then write the name on your own.

Percy

Say the word at the top of each box. Then fill in the missing letters.

will

＿ill

wi＿＿＿

find

f＿＿＿d

＿＿＿nd

we

＿＿

＿e

Say the word at the top of each box. Then fill in the missing letters.

could	see
coul__	__ __ee
c__ __ __ld	s__ __ __

Read the words in the box. Then read the sentences. Find the word in the box that correctly completes each sentence. Write the word on the line.

_____

Perdy _____ not see.

He could _____ see.

He could not _____ Perdy.

_____ could see.

not
He
could
see

217

Say the word at the top of each box. Then fill in the missing letters.

five	of
__ive	o__
f____e	

were	in
we__e	__n
____re	

there	
____ere	
th__r__	

218

Say the word at the top of each box. Then fill in the missing letters.

not	stop
__ __	__ __
__ot	sto__
__ __ __	__ __ __
n__ __ __	__ __op

Read the words in the box. Then read the sentences. Find the word in the box that correctly completes each sentence. Write the word on the line.

_____ could stop.

They _____ not stop.

They will _____.

We will _____ stop there.

could

not

They

stop

219

Say the word at the top of each box. Then fill in the missing letters.

always	eat
___ ___ ___	___ ___ __t
___ ___ ways	___ ___
alw ___ ___ s	ea ___

Read the words in the box. Then read the sentences. Find the word in the box that correctly completes each sentence. Write the word on the line.

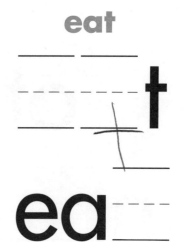

_____

_____ always eat.

_____

They _____ eat.

_____

They _____ .

_____

They _____ stop.

always
always
They
eat
could

Read the words in the box. Then read the sentences. Find the word in the box that correctly completes each sentence. Write the word on the line.

_____ was a show.

There _____ a show.

_____ was it?

Five of them were in ____ show.

What a _____ it was!

What
was
a
show
It

Say the word at the top of each box. Then fill in the missing letters.

wish

wi _____

_____ h

could

c _ u _ d

c _____ d

find

f _____ d

f _____

them

th _____

_____ m

Pongo

P _____ go

P _ ng _____

Read the words in the box. Then read the sentences. Find the word in the box that correctly completes each sentence. Write the word on the line.

_____ will help.

She will _____ .

I _____ help them.

I will help _____ .

"I will help," she _____ .

_____ will help you.

help
I
you
She
will
said

Trace the name with your pencil. Then write the name on your own.

Pongo

Read the words in the box. Then read the sentences. Find the word in the box that correctly completes each sentence. Write the word on the line.

"_____

_____ , no!" said Pongo.

"Oh, _____ !" said Pongo.

_____ will help.

"Oh, Pongo!" Perdy _____ .

said

no

Pongo

Oh

Perdy

wish

they

a

them

he

said

I

show

© Disney

Pongo

© Disney

there

© Disney

we

© Disney

she

© Disney

you

© Disney

it

© Disney

could

© Disney

will

were

oh

find

no

see

in

not

was

stop

help

always

eat

of

what

five

ANSWER KEY

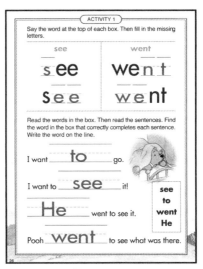

Page 26

Page 27

Page 28

Page 29

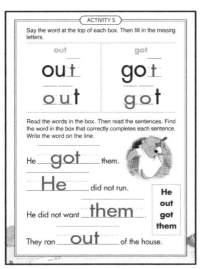

Page 30

Page 31

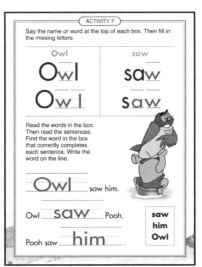

Page 32

Page 33

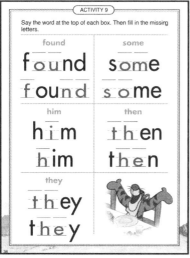

Page 34

233

ANSWER KEY

ACTIVITY 1

Trace the words with a pencil.
Then write the words on your own.

Fall Fall
fall fall
Wind Wind
wind wind

Page 64

ACTIVITY 2

Trace the names with your pencil. Then write the names on your own.

Pooh Pooh
Piglet Piglet

Read the words in the box. Then read the sentences. Find the word in the box that correctly completes each sentence. Write the word on the line.

Pooh is here.

Here is Piglet.

Come here," I said.

I will come.

**Come
Piglet
Pooh
I**

Page 65

ACTIVITY 3

Say the word at the top of each box. Then fill in the missing letters.

will	on
will	on
will	on
hold	**said**
hold	said
hold	said
Pooh	
Pooh	
Pooh	

Page 66

ACTIVITY 4

Trace the words with your pencil. Then write the words on your own.

Hold Hold
hold hold

Read the words in the box. Then read the sentences. Find the word in the box that correctly completes each sentence. Write the word on the line.

"Hold on," they said

They did hold on.

They will hold on.

They did hold on.

**hold
They
said
on**

Page 67

ACTIVITY 5

Say the word at the top of each box. Then fill in the missing letters.

not	do
not	do
to	**want**
to	want
said	
said	

Page 68

ACTIVITY 6

Trace the name.   Fill in the missing letters.

Owl   Owl
Owl   Owl
Owl

Write the name.

Owl
Owl

Page 69

ACTIVITY 7

Read the words in the box. Then read the sentences. Find the word in the box that correctly completes each sentence. Write the word on the line.

**said
too
Pooh
would
like**

I like Pooh.

Pooh would like some.

I would like some, too.

"I want some to," Pooh said.

"I like Piglet," Pooh said

Page 70

ACTIVITY 8

Say the word at the top of each box. Then fill in the missing letters.

they	came
they	came
down	**with**
down	with
it	
it	

Page 71

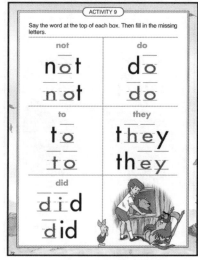

ACTIVITY 9

Say the word at the top of each box. Then fill in the missing letters.

not	do
not	do
to	**they**
to	they
did	
did	

Page 72

ANSWER KEY

Page 102

Page 103

Page 104

Page 105

Page 106

Page 107

Page 108

Page 109

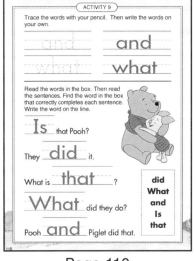

Page 110

ANSWER KEY

Page 140

Page 141

Page 142

Page 143

Page 144

Page 145

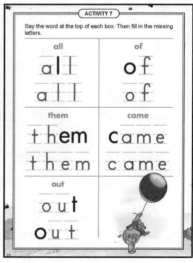

Page 146

Page 147

Page 148

ANSWER KEY

Page 178

Page 179

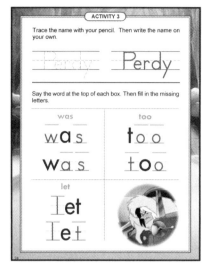

Page 180

Page 181

Page 182

Page 183

Page 184

Page 185

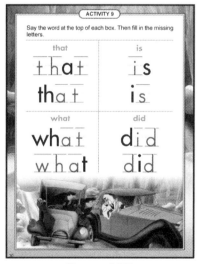

Page 186

ANSWER KEY

Page 216

Page 217

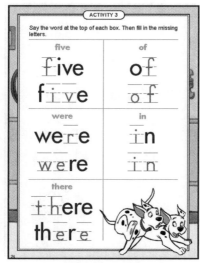

Page 218

Page 219

Page 220

Page 221

Page 222

Page 223

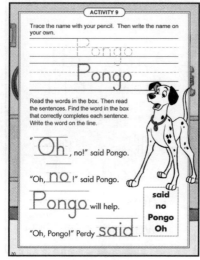

Page 224